The Story of
Clan Mingin

(The smelliest clan in Scotland!)

Alison Mary Fitt & Willie Ritchie

Design - Melvin Creative
Printed in China

Published by
GW Publishing
PO Box 6091
Thatcham
Berks
RG19 8XZ.

Tel + 44 (0)1635 268080
www.gwpublishing.com

ISBN 978-0-9561211-9-6

The Story of
Clan Mingin

(The smelliest clan in Scotland!)

If Scots words are new to you turn over and look,
you'll find them explained at the back of the book!

Publishing

A long time ago, some very grimy, very smelly people lived in a Scottish glen called Glen Mingin. They were known as Clan Mingin because they smelt something awful. It wasn't their fault they ponged so much. For years on end, there had been no water in the burn to wash themselves or their clothes in.

The reason there was no water in the burn was because Lord Muck, who lived in Castle Muck, had asked an inventor friend to make a strange machine called a water pincher. Every day, this weird but wonderful contraption drained the water out of the burn, and sucked it up into the castle. There, the water was heated in great big tanks.

There was plenty of water, too, for washing up Lord Muck's dinner dishes. So every evening, he enjoyed a great big banquet using every dish he had. Then he told his servants to wash each goblet, serving dish and platter, three times - and then rinse them another three times! "Fill the sink with fresh water each time," he ordered them.

Of course, it also meant that there wasn't a drop of water left for the Clan Mingin. No wonder they stank so badly. Their pong drifted to neighbouring clans round about, and even the council had been sent round to complain.

It wasn't surprising that other clans kept well away from them. If any neighbouring clansmen had the misfortune to meet Clan Mingin in the hills, they held their noses and hurried on as fast as they could.

It was horrible being so smelly. Grimy Gordon, the Clan Chief, was forever begging Lord Muck to leave them some water.

It looked like greedy Lord Muck was going to go on draining the burn. "Right," said Grimy Gordon grimly. "We can't go on ponging like a field of rotten turnips. Let's ask Clan Bonnie in the next glen if **they** will spare us some water."

Clan Mingin went home gloomily. "If only we had water to wash in," they sighed. Then one day, a rider on horseback brought Grimy Gordon a message.

Grimy Gordon read it and beamed. "Clan Kindly has given us an old whisky barrel full of water," he told his clansmen. "They have left it for us to collect, a mile away from their glen."

Before they could catch up with it, the barrel crashed into a dyke and split open. All the water gushed out. "We're in big trouble," they wailed.

Next day, the Chief had an idea. "There might be an underground spring somewhere," he said. "If we can find one, we would have loads of water." So the clansmen with the strongest arms started to dig.

The clansmen promised to be careful. But they were soon flinging mud everywhere again...

He got such a shock, he overbalanced and sat down in a disgustingly sploshy, revoltingly smelly cow's pancake. As it happened, Lord Muck had been on his way to welcome his posh friends, the Earl and Countess of Edinburgh, who he had invited for lunch. He was in a right panic.

Just then, the Earl and Countess of Edinburgh arrived. "How dare you greet us in such a revolting state?" roared the Earl. "You look as though you've been rolling around in the castle piggery!"

Lord Muck's visitors soon swept off. "Come, my dear," sniffed the Earl. "There is no way we are dining with a midden like him! Who knows if his dishes are clean to eat from?"

Clan Mingin couldn't help laughing. But Grimy Gordon said they must apologise to Lord Muck. After all, it was one of **them** that had flung the spadeful of mud!

But much to their surprise, Lord Muck apologised to them! "Now I know what it feels like to be grimy and smelly, and have people holding their noses. It's horribly humiliating," he muttered. "Will you forgive me for being so greedy and taking all the water?" "Aye, alright," said Clan Mingin. "As long as you leave plenty for us in future!" Lord Muck promised he would.

The next morning, the burn was full of water again. But it wasn't **cold** water. It was lovely **warm** water, which was being wooshed back down into the burn at the turn of a knob.

Clan Mingin soaped and rubbed and scrubbed until every bit of muck and grime was gone. Soon they all smelt as sweet as the heather and instead of being the smelliest, grimiest clan, they became the cleanest clan in Scotland!

Some words you need to know...

burn	means stream
oor	means our
dicht	means wash
tae	means toe, or too
sookin	means sucking
nane	means none
isna	means isn't
mair	means more
midnicht	means midnight
disna	means doesn't
semmit	means vest
whaur	means where
yir	means your

wudna	means wouldn't
mingin	means very smelly
guff	means stink
hing aboot	means hang about
wha	means who
tak	means take
mingers	means very smelly people
hae	means have
nae	means no
dinna	means don't
guid	means good
shooglin	means splashing
numpties	means idiots
tichter	means tighter
clartie	means very grimy
heid	means head
ca cannie	means be careful
manky	means dirty and smelly
doon	means down
richt	means right
braw	means great

Grimy Gordon
explains...